When Lawn

With best wishes

(signed with Flymo's quill)

First published October 1992

Burcombe Publishing, 1, Burcombe Villas, Chalford Hill,
Stroud, Gloucestershire, GL6 8BN

Typeset in New Century Schoolbook using Ventura Publisher.

Printed by:

    Quacks, 7, Grape Lane, Petergate, York, YO1 2HU

ISBN 0 9519422 0 4

British Library CIP Data: A catalogue record for this book is
available from the British Library.

When Lawnmowers Fly

by

Graham Hobbs

Illustrated by

Pupils from Thomas Keble School

Acknowledgements

No one person writes a book. Thanks to all those friends and family who supported me and encouraged me to see this one into print. Especial thanks must go to my father-in-law, Edmond Searing, for his editing skills and my brother-in-law, Keith Searing, for his technical support. The front cover was the work of Anita Reardon, Head of Art at Thomas Keble School, Eastcombe, near Stroud. Special congratulations must go to her pupils, who produced the illustrations. The young artists have shown remarkable talent.

Thank you, too, to all those people and organisations who inspired incidents and allowed me to refer to them or their experiences.

Lastly, I cannot neglect to acknowledge those creatures who not only passed through our garden, but our lives as well. Their antics initiated much of this story.

Graham Hobbs, Chalford Hill, March 1992

1. T.L.C.

For thirty-five days an egg, three times the weight of a hen's egg, had been in an incubator in a barn in the Brecon hills of South Wales. The egg was plain white, except for a cross pencilled in on the upper side. A hand reached in and picked it up.

"I don't give much for this one's chances. It's overdue for coming out. Look you now, most of the goslings running around over there hatched from eggs that were put in the incubator after this one."

"How do you know if this one was any good anyway, Grandad?" asked the visitor.

"I candled it."

"What's that?"

"Come over here and I'll show you."

The old man and the small boy went over to an old trestle table on which was a candle. He lit it.

"When I was a boy almost every poulty farmer used a real candle like this. Most folk use an electric light these days. It's supposed to be better and safer. Still, I've always found a candle good enough and I haven't burnt the barn down yet. Now if I hold the egg in front of the flame, what can you see?"

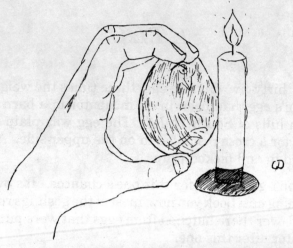

"The outside edges are lighter and there's a funny shape filling up most of the middle. The bottom bit looks a bit lighter too."

"Quite right. It's a bit vaguer than it was earlier. When I first did this I could see blood vessels even. Then as time went on I could see the little gosling forming. You use this technique to watch the egg develop and you can even tell if the bird has died. This one had been alright up till now."

"What do you think went wrong?"

"I'm pretty certain about that. In the bottom of the incubator is a tray that's supposed to be topped up with water. The water evaporates and makes the air moist. Moist air stops the eggs drying out. I even spray the eggs with water sometimes. It simulates the mother goose coming back wet from a swim and sitting on the eggs again. Well, anyway, a few days back we had one of those days when a lot of things went wrong. Not least was the milking machine breaking down; I had to finish the last

2

forty-two cows by hand instead. By the time I'd finished I had only one thought on my mind - bed. I clean forgot to top up the water tray. I had so much clearing up to do the next day that I forgot all about the incubator till that night. The eggs had dried and one gosling had died. Another one was looking pretty parched but it recovered after a long guzzle and a bit of T.L.C."

"What's that?"

"Tender, loving care. Well I reckon all that neglect is what's done for this one. I lost three others over that incident."

"What's this circle on the shell?"

"The one on the other side to the cross, you mean? It's a way of knowing which side is uppermost. A mother goose turns the eggs over regularly every day. I suppose it spreads the warmth around, but it's not just that. If we don't do the same, the eggs don't develop right. The young bird often sticks to the side of the shell and can't grow or move or something. That's the other thing I didn't do when the system went wrong last week. I should have put the eggs circle side up that night and cross side up in the morning. My forgetting must have helped finish them off."

"That isn't the mark I mean, Grandad. It's this one on the end."

"Which one's that, David? Well look at that now! That's not a pencil mark, - it's a crack! The poor little thing was alive after all! I don't suppose it still is. Can't think why I didn't notice that crack before."

3

"Perhaps it was because it wasn't there. Grandad! Do you think it could be trying to hatch after all? I mean it might still be alive despite being dried out and stuck to the side and unable to move and too late to hatch and I'm sure I can hear it cheeping!"

"Wishful thinking! Not very likely but ... Oh well, if it keeps you happy we'll take it into the kitchen. There's a better table and more light. We'll give it a closer examination."

Excited, David ran ahead of his grandad to the kitchen and fumbled with the handle on the door. Unfortunately, little boys who are in that frame of mind can only concentrate on one thing at a time. The large egg slipped from the small hand. David made a grab for it but only succeeded in knocking it further away from himself.

The precious object struck the ground a glancing blow and rolled on. Tears were streaming down David's face even before his grandad, who had not been far behind, came on the scene.

David gingerly picked up the broken egg in his trembling hands.

"I'm sorry, Grandad."

Salt water was now dropping onto the bits of yellow downy feather sticking out of the cracks in the shell.

"... didn't mean to ... that is, I ... it was ..."

The words faded away.

"That's alright son. It was probably dead already. Anyhow, I'll tell you a secret. I didn't want to disappoint you but I've had geese, ducks and other fowl for more than fifty years and I've never known anyone get a live little one out of its shell by helping it. If they can't get out by themselves they never get out. Here let me take it. You'll need to wash your hands and then how about a cup of tea? Perhaps you can come and watch me milk the cows? Your dad always liked to help with that any time. Or how about watching the telly ? I'm sure there's some good cartoons on about now or ... or ..."

Grandad had stopped, not because he was running out of ideas to take the little lad's mind off the tragedy; rather, something else had taken his attention. Having relieved David of the mangled remains, he thought he detected a slight movement.

"No. It can't be. Surely not. It is! I don't believe it but it is! Look, David! There's movement inside this damaged shell. I'm sure there is. Come on! Let's get it inside quickly and see what shape it's in."

A lot happened in the next hour and a half, apart from Grandad forgetting to start milking the cows. The kitchen had the atmosphere of an operating theatre with some tense emergency surgery going on.

"Tweezers!" said Grandad.

"Tweezers," said David.

"Good. Brush!" said Grandad.

"Brush," said David.

"A bit more light over here!" said Grandad.

5

"More light," said David.

"Tissue!" said Grandad.

"Tissue," said David.

"Brandy!"

"Brandy? Where's that and what do you need it for?"

"It's the stuff in the bottle over there. Pour me out about half a glass and don't drop it like you did the egg! It's a very expensive and useful medicine. Cures a lot of things."

The gosling's medicine arrived but David was a little surprised when Grandad drank it instead. Still, he must have had his reasons. It certainly seemed to perk him up.

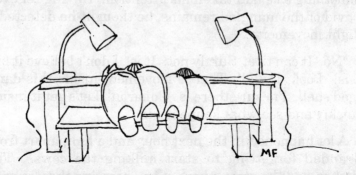

By the time Grandma returned from town, wondering why the cows were congregating up at the unused milk parlour, the scene in the kitchen was quite unlike anything she had seen before. One corner of the table had an old newspaper laid across it and laid across that was a pile of shell fragments. At either end of the table was a lamp. Both were focusing on something in the middle of the table but she could not see what. The rest of the view was obscured by a big bottom with a pair of muddy boots pointing out from below, all mounted above a kitchen bench. A miniature version of the same spectacle was beside it. She was not pleased. Neither would her daughter be. Her make-up kit was being used, along with sundry other household items, as surgical instruments in a very messy operation.

So it was that a little Brecon Buff gosling entered the world against all the odds. She was mostly yellow where her fluffy down had not been torn off, stuck to bits of shell and membrane. Such feathers as remained on her head and wings were darker. Her bill was pink and so were her webbed feet, including the claws, apart from the middle one on the right. That one was missing altogether and would never grow again. The most curious feature she had, though, was her tail. It was pointing off at ninety degrees to the left. That was another thing that would never change. It was a miserable start to life but at least it was a start.

If Grandma had had her way, it would have been an end too. She felt that it was cruel to keep such an injured and deformed creature alive, especially when it was in pain and only just holding its own in the battle for survival. It would probably be dead by morning anyway so why not put it out of its misery straight away? To give her her due, her attitude was clouded. The lack of preparation while she had been out, the mess in the kitchen and the sound of lowing cows desperate to be milked had not helped, and it was this pathetic creature's fault.

However, two other people, who had spent nearly two hours of intense T.L.C. on the little creature, were not going to see their efforts wasted. The issue of her survival had become a personal crusade to them, and conviction usually wins an argument against annoyance.

7

That night, the new gosling, now known as Flymo, because hopefully she would soon be skimming over the grass and shortening it, had a well earned sleep on some sawdust in a box in David's room. There was a dish of water, and what bits of it she did not spill, she made good use of to restore her depleted body. A table lamp was poised overhead. It did not disturb her sleep but whenever she felt cold she limped over to it to soak up its heat. When David woke up the next morning it was quite clear that she was going to make it after all. She had every right to. Significantly enough, printed on the side of her box was:

The company's initials were T.L.C.

2. A Wild Life

Let's leave Flymo in Wales and travel north to the Arctic, Iceland to be exact. Here another of her kind was entering the world in very different circumstances.

Eric was a gander. His hatching had not been as dramatic as Flymo's. Not that it wasn't hard work for a little fellow. It was. He had to strain with most of his muscles and chip away with his bill. Nevertheless, with relatively few problems, he emerged from his dark home into a world of almost continuous light. In that part of the northern hemisphere, the sun is in evidence for over twenty hours a day in summer.

He felt tired. His eyes found even the weak Icelandic sun hard to adjust to. Strangely, the nudging around by his mother's bill did not worry him. It was so like the way she had nudged him around as an egg that he felt secure and relaxed. He snuggled under her down, free from the cold wind and the seemingly bright light and did the most natural thing. He slept.

Just as he had done in his earlier private world of the eggshell, he dreamed. Till now, his dreams had always been cosy imaginings but after a time he started to have memories of pushing and pecking at the tough lime wall, the experience he had had an hour earlier. He felt the harsh force of the light as he remembered how it hit his eyes with such strength. In his excitement he awoke, cheeping. His noise and movement was the cue for his mother to stand up and let him free.

The light returned. He blinked hard at first but slowly felt able to bear it. It was a strange sensation. There were dark and light patches and shades in between. In only a few minutes he was beginning to distinguish shapes. This became easier as his eyes learned how to focus. They adjusted to distant objects at first, then the middle distance. Before the light faded for the dull, dusky period that made the so-called night in that part of the world, Eric had been able to make out items nearer to him. Like many greylags, his sight had its limitations. True, he could make out many objects hundreds of yards away and do so in colour as well, yet very close up he found things less distinct. This was due, in part, to having eyes on the side of his head. It was very important that they should be so placed. They gave him a very wide view of the world and that panoramic vision helped him keep an eye out for predators.

The disadvantage was in looking at things just in front of you. When your eyes face in completely opposite directions, there is little they can both focus on together. Soon he found it easier to concentrate on items with just one eye. It was not hard to ignore what the other one saw.

It does not worry a goose to be looked at with one eye but it is an unfortunate trait from the human point of view. Whenever a goose takes an interest in people, it tends to concentrate on them with one eye. The cocked head and haughty single-eyed stare combine to give an apparently unfriendly leer at the best of times. It does not help their unfriendly reputation. It is a quirk of human nature that such a posture is condemned in a goose but considered cute in a duck.

10

The world was introducing other experiences to Eric besides light. Sound was the main one. It was not entirely new, because he had detected it for several days before hatching. One particular sound, his mother's voice, was quickly recognised. It was one he had been especially aware of and now it was much clearer. She in her turn had quickly adapted to his plaintive note. They became so in tune with each other that they could recognise each other's call above the honking of hundreds of competitors.

As all the sights, sounds, feelings and smells grew on his awareness, Eric learned about his environment.

His home was an untidy arrangement of dead grass and other vegetation. It was perched on a mound, projecting above a sea of green sphagnum moss which hid the marshy surroundings. Patches of grass sprouted round about. For some distance there were other mounds supporting more families of noisy greylags.

 To begin with, Eric shared his nest with his mother and a much heavier bird who tended to come and go a bit and argue with the neighbours. That was his father. There were four unhatched eggs occupying much of the space. He saw little of these, as his mother sat on them most of the time. He preferred life snuggled under her wing. Within a couple of days three of the eggs had become Eric's sisters. The last one did not do anything at all. It was not long

before all the shuffling about in the nest caused it to roll down into the floating moss. A passing webbed foot carelessly completed its removal from the scene.

The four goslings soon adapted to their arctic neighbourhood. Within a week, they were nibbling at grass and other vegetation. They would even wander several yards from home to do so. They could swim when necessary, despite only having downy feathers and no natural waterproofing. They oiled themselves from their mother's gland as they preened and soon made themselves waterproof. Soon they were not only putting on weight but replacing their fluffy down with proper feathers. They appeared rather odd with small quills projecting out of their furry looking down, neither proper goslings nor geese.

The adults were also experiencing a feather change. The previous year's feathers were being shed, so such quills and down that the wind did not blow away covered much of the nests. This was a serious time. With the old flight feathers coming loose and the new ones not properly formed, the birds were flightless. Their hunters knew it. Almost daily whole families fled panicking into the safety of the deeper open water edging the boggy neighbourhood. Often it was a false alarm, but once one or two began honking and running, the whole community took up the hue and cry. In spite of the seeming confusion, the families regrouped with few problems and would find their way back together when they felt less nervous. It was towards the end of this period, when some birds were just starting to get airborne again, that Eric had his first really nasty experience in life.

A cunning arctic fox had managed to get much closer than usual before the warning of the more observant birds set the exodus in motion. Eric's family suffered from being one of the furthest from the open water and, on this occasion, closest to the fox. It was his father in fact who first raised the alarm, but for once he did not run. That was because Eric was between him and the enemy. Even though the rest of the flock were stampeding noisily away and Eric's mother was calling frantically, Eric could only concentrate on the animal in front of him. He was entranced. He had never seen such a creature before. It was about half a yard in length with its tail half as long again. It had a grey-brown coat and was poised, front legs along the ground with head between them, ready to spring. The dark eyes were fixed on Eric.

What followed was etched into Eric's mind. His father interposed himself between Eric and the hunter. For several seconds, neither animal moved. Both faced each other, head lowered to the ground. The gander ruffled his feathers to look bigger and hissed a warning.

This was a surprise. At other times the fox might have backed off, content with less formidable prey or even carrion. A dead seal washed up on the beach could be equally appetising and could feed several families for many days. Now though, he had seven hungry cubs and a mate to help feed, and both game and carrion had been scarcer this year. He could not afford to be put off. He sprang.

Eric's father hardly saw him coming and the next thing he knew he had been seized by his long neck. He could not reach to bite his attacker but pounded him heavily with his powerfully built wings. Eric watched, frustrated. In anger he wanted to peck and hit this intruder but could not move for fear. He simply stayed put as his father was dragged away, still beating incessantly at his enemy. The protagonists were in a patch of water now and the hammering wings were making sweeping splashes, though not for long. The splashes became smaller and less frequent. In less than a minute they stopped for good and, though battered and bruised, the fox dragged the carcass away with a lot more ease.

Up until that moment, Eric had never respected his father. He had always viewed him as a noisy bully, belligerent with all other geese and even prone to pecking at his mate. His children were justifiably scared of him and did not miss him when he was not around. There was little one could say in his favour. Till now, that was. Through Eric's stunned mind came the realisation that his father was not as uncaring or stupid as he appeared. If he had not taken on the highly unfair challenge, Eric himself would have been the victim.

Slowly, the crowd returned, along with the rest of the family. They all felt uneasy but the everyday pressures of living and growing took over.

In a few short months a much bigger Eric was flying south with the flock, to escape the severe arctic winter which would take over the area where he had grown up. It was a flight of several hundred miles in which he would looe a lot of weight as he burnt up his reserves of fat. It would end in the inevitable gooselike way, with a lot of noise, as they landed on the estuaries around Britain. Eric, simply following the crowd, did not know that yet.

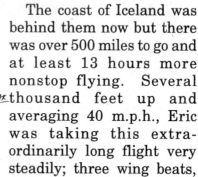

The coast of Iceland was behind them now but there was over 500 miles to go and at least 13 hours more nonstop flying. Several thousand feet up and averaging 40 m.p.h., Eric was taking this extra-ordinarily long flight very steadily; three wing beats, breathe on the fourth, three wing beats, breathe on the fourth, three wing beats and so on. With the rhythm established he could think. One thing stood out, his father's sacrifice. In time to come, Eric would face the same situation.

3. Sheep, Rabbits, Goats and Geese.

While Eric is winging his way south, the story moves in the same direction, to Gloucestershire. A range of hills known as the Cotswolds sweep across the county. These uplands are cut into by many sharp valleys which have several villages climbing the sides of them, notably around Stroud. In one of these villages, James and Emma Stewart and their children, Daniel, Jane and Fiona, had recently moved into a large Victorian house. Things were looking good for them. There was much more room than in the little twelve foot wide terraced cottage they had just moved out of. James had a good job teaching juniors, and his offspring were delighted with the village school. Already they were bringing friends home to play in their new 150 foot garden.

However, all was not well. James had not been able to shake off a bout of 'flu', which one of his pupils had innocently passed on. Months later he was still feeling weak. Not to worry though. He was content at that moment, surveying the garden of his new house with pleasure. Two rows of newly planted fruit trees stretched down it. James had been short of stamina but, by planting them one a day, he had the satisfaction of a job well done. There was little else that would need doing to them now, apart from occasional pruning. Unfortunately, the same could not be said of the grass. Even with an electric mower it had taken a week to cut it once. Perhaps a more natural lawnmower was called for.

"Here, Keith," he had asked his cousin, "how many sheep have you got?"

"About forty Jacobs and a few others."

"What do you keep them for? It's not your main job so why have you got them?"

"We've got several acres of orchards attached to the house. We use them to keep the grass an inch high and clear up the windfalls. They save hours of work and produce wool in the process."

"That sounds like the answer to my problem. How many sheep would I need on just a quarter of an acre of orchard?"

"I wouldn't bother. You would probably only manage about three lambs. Then you wouldn't want to get rid of them. The children would become too attached to them and hand reared lambs grow up thinking they're supposed to be a daft form of human. Then you've got all the regulations about dipping, movement of livestock and so on. If I'd known what was involved I'd have never started. You've got too many reasons not to start yourself. What's wrong with an ordinary lawnmower?"

"The land is on a slope and is some kind of archaeological site, with bits of old walls and other buried debris making the surface uneven. The sort of machine you ride around on wouldn't work and I can't use a hover mower because it takes too long. What with schoolwork and other things, I simply haven't got the time these days."

"Well if that's your problem you'll have to look at some other kind of grass nibbler   I can't tell you much about any of those. Do you know anyone who's had experience with rabbits or goats?"

James did know someone who had some very memorable experience of rabbits. It was himself. As the memories came flooding back he did not want a repeat of that labour saving attempt.

In those days, it was a similar problem. There was so little time to dig, weed and cultivate a 90 foot long vegetable patch. Why not borrow a pair of pet rabbits from a friend? They could eat the weeds and manure the ground. They loved digging too. They could spend their whole time doing it. When they had finished one patch, their pen could be moved on to the next.

Sadly, it did not work like that. When Reginald and Belinda arrived they clearly did not have a taste for the sort of weeds they were offered. They also seemed to produce any manure at night when they were back in their hutch. Finally Belinda actually got round to digging. It was a small hole, straight down into the earth. The rest of the pen was not being cleared. In fact, it was half a rabbit deep in compost, hedge trimmings and old cabbage stumps thrown in by well meaning neighbours. The pair could stand this kind of treatment no longer and Reginald began digging a hole, right under the pen. This was more like it. Fresh lettuce, cabbage, carrots; you name it, and all the neighbours in the row of cottages seemed to be growing it. They had also been kind enough not to fence their patches in either. What more could a rabbit want?

Conversely, what less could a neighbour want? James was just settling down to a pile of marking, having put Jane back into bed for the third time. The rabbits had

frustrated him and now she was the last straw. If she got up again without a good reason she would get a big smack. She reappeared.

"Daddy, the white rabbit is in the garden, eating carrots."

Having just been reading "Alice in Wonderland", James felt that his imaginative daughter had gone too far this time. She was about to receive her smack, when it dawned on him what had happened.

With a cry of despair, he ran out into the vegetable patch, in time to meet several neighbours armed with assorted weapons charging over the remains of their crops in an attempt to deal with the vandals. Various dogs were joining in but getting in the way more than helping. On a popularity scale of nought to ten, the rabbits had gone from ten down to nought in about as many minutes. James himself, had gone off the scale completely. The rabbits went back the next day.

How about a goat? The books seemed to be very encouraging about them. They appeared to eat everything, from grass to rubbish, and turn it into a gallon of milk every day. Moreover this milk was supposed to be better than a cow's, there were no regulations concerning the animal or its dairy products and you could even take a goat for walks, just like a dog. Something did not sound right though. James' first and last close up experience with a goat had been with Cleopatra, who kept the grass down at the Baptist Church graveyard, in Chalford. She had seemed very inquisitive about him, and friendly too, so he scratched her behind the ear. He had not known she had a sore patch just there and his attempt to be friendly got a quick reply, right in the stomach. No, there had to be more to it than the books said so he went to talk to a friend round the corner. He had had a goat to keep his unmanageable grass down.

"Yes, we had a billy called Munch, when we lived at Painswick. He didn't do a very satisfactory job. We had him chained to a stake but he'd only eat the grass when the chain was stretched to its full length. We ended up with grazed circles amongst areas of long grass and that was when the stake stayed in. The soil was so thin before you came to the rock that we weren't able to hammer it in very far. Munch was strong enough to pull it out quite easily; then he'd go exploring. That's when life got interesting. He had a special liking for the neighbour's peach tree."

"So goats like peaches?"

"I don't know about that. It never got as far as producing any fruit. Munch ate the whole tree. I don't think the neighbour would have minded if he'd stopped there but Munch had a liking for washing lines too. That includes the washing, by the way. Fortunately, they hadn't hung any out but the plastic cord hanging from the rotary washing line was too much of a temptation. It looked like spaghetti by the time we found him.

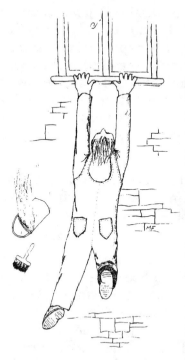

"What finally upset the neighbours was when the painter resigned. He was minding his own business painting the bathroom window, when Munch took an inexplicable dislike to the man's ladder. He charged it full pelt, got his head stuck between the rungs, panicked and ran off with it round his neck.

"The painter was left hanging onto the windowsill until rescued. He hadn't seen who'd done it but we couldn't blame it on the local youth having a practical joke. The evidence was indisputable, and as a magistrate I should know. Munch's normally brown bottom had changed to white gloss!

"After those neighbours moved away, things went well for a while until Munch became addicted to tarred roofing felt. He found that by standing on the bank behind the new neighbour's shed, he could reach the roof and strip the felt off. To be fair it did need reroofing and he spat out the nails but the owner, a retired colonel, wasn't grateful.

'Ah know what Ah'm talking about sah!' he said. 'Ah hed a goat for a regimental mascot. He was properleh disciplined. A spell in the armeh is what this brute wants. That'd soon sort him out!'

"Somehow, even in retirement, the Colonel couldn't change from his army ways. He laid out his garden like a parade ground. All his flowers were planted in military formations, with perfectly straight lines and at distances measured with a ruler. He had a beautiful single row of tulips, his 'Thin Red Line' he called it, in honour of the Battle of Balaclava or something. The morning he came round to see me, he'd have challenged me to a duel, if it had still been legal.

'Sah!' he shouted, very red in the face. 'Yair goat has done what the whole Russian cavalreh couldn't. He's massacring may Thin Red Line. Come and see, at the double!'

"Sure enough, Munch was methodically working his way along the line, biting off the head of each flower in turn, leaving a row of neatly clipped green stalks. By now we'd realised that colonels and goats didn't mix, so we gave the billy to a farmer who wanted some scrub on a rough pasture kept down. Mind you, he made a parting gesture to the old boy next door. The fellow thought his silk scarf must have blown off the washing line one day. Truth to tell I wasn't in time to stop the last corner disappearing down the goat's throat."

"So having a goat to keep the grass down in the orchard isn't that straightforward?"

"I'll say not. If it's a nanny she'll need milking regularly twice a day whether you're ill, on holiday or unable to face the weather. Either sort will only flatten the grass and eat the trees. Worse, I forgot to mention how badly a billy stinks. Do you remember that song from 'The Sound of Music', 'High on a hill stood a lonely goat-herd'? It was after we got our first whiff of a billy we understood very well why he was lonely!"

The problem of the ever lengthening grass was still on James' mind as he and the dog walked past a house. It was always amusing to watch what happened here - a parrot in the porch usually whistled at any dog that came past and then called out "Come on! Here boy!" As expected, it happened today and the dog was fooled into returning. Laughing, James turned to admire the parrot.

"Want to come in and meet 'im?" asked the owner. "Come in. Don't mind the goose. 'Er won't 'urt. She'm a useless guard but 'er doz a lovely job of keeping the grass down."

"Does what?" said James.

4. Rejection

It's no good putting it off. He's going to have to find out sooner or later. The sooner he knows, the sooner he'll get over it."

"Alright, I'll talk to him when he gets home. Oh help! Here he comes now."

David had come straight in from school and gone straight into the garden to the former rabbit hutch, now occupied by Flymo.

"Ah, David. I'd like to have a word with you about our going out to live in Canada."

"Yes Dad, I'm listening," said David as he helped his pet out of the hutch.

"Listening but not concentrating," thought Dad.

"It's about Flymo too."

"What's up?" David asked, with a worried expression.

He was certainly paying attention now. Flymo and going to live in Canada were two thoughts that had already met in his mind. He had tried not to think about them at the same time because he could guess the outcome.

"Well, Mum and I have been thinking about the goose's future. It's not possible to take her with us. No, please don't interrupt. I'm sorry. I know she means a lot to you and everything but it just isn't on. She'll soon outgrow that rabbit hutch, even before we go, and the garden really isn't big enough for her. Grandad can't have her back because he's retiring and selling up the farm. That's why we wanted you to have a last holiday there. I've even checked with the new owner. He doesn't want any geese because they aren't money-makers. Those that are left will soon be used for Christmas, so at  least she's escaped that. She'll simply have to find a new home. Yes, I know how you feel but there it is. We can always get you a new and better pet when we've settled down. Yes, that's what we'll do. We'll get you another goose. They must have thousands of Canada geese in Canada, just like the ones on the lake in the park, you know, the friendly ones that come and eat the bread out of your hand."

David did not want to hear this. He clutched his treasure closer to him. He had seen this coming and had tried to push it to the back of his mind, but there was no escape. Doing that to problems does not solve them. They have to be faced sooner or later. He could not say anything so let his feelings out in the only way he could. Not for the first time he wept about Flymo. His whole body shook. Why did this have to happen? He had done everything a person could to make this precious creature his. He had brought her into the world against all the odds, fed her carefully, kept her properly housed and spent hours simply petting and talking to her. He read all the books that the library could produce on geese and reckoned he knew more about them than any other child in Gloucestershire. She may have been the ugliest, most deformed domestic goose in the country but David believed she was the most loved. What was going to happen to her? Summoning up his bravest effort he fixed his watery eyes on his father's. His voice shook more than his body.

"What's going to happen to her?" he quaked.

This was worse than Dad had expected. Thank goodness he had anticipated that question and had worked out an answer.

"We've already fixed that. An acquaintance of mine has a smallholding just outside Gloucester. He's coming for her tonight. He's got a dozen geese himself. He says he'll happily give a home to her. She'll have lots of company then, with a proper house and a large area to roam around on. It'll be more natural for her ... um, look, would you like to say your goodbyes to her now? I'll, um, call you in for tea when it's ready. Yes, er, see you later."

Dad beat a hasty retreat. He had hopelessly mishandled it. Was it really sensible to have presented the child with the instant loss of his pet? Shouldn't he have told him and then given him a few days to adjust? Perhaps he should have told him earlier. There again, it would only have made him miserable earlier. Despite a lot of practice, it had been harder for him to say what he had to than for his son to hear it. The sight of the hurt, which he felt he had caused, was making him weepy himself, so he had backed out of the situation as soon as he could. He too had grown attached to the bird and did not want to see her go.

Some people do not understand children's feelings. It's small wonder then that most people never realise how animals feel. Yet the truth is that a lot of animals can be even more sensitive than we are. Flymo was no exception.

What kind of an image does a goose convey to you? A clumsy one? A stupid one? Isn't the expression "Bird-brained" rather apt? If you've ever met a goose in real life, you probably remember it as a noisy and aggressive brute. But think. Do you know any people like that? Even they still have feelings. Deep down they want to be accepted, appreciated and valued. Flymo had feelings too, and she understood what the recent conversation meant. The happy world she had known since hatching was about to be shattered. She savoured every moment of David's cuddle, knowing that this person who was so devoted to her was about to be separated from her forever. All too soon he returned her to the hutch and closed the door. She stared as the sobbing figure retreated into the house, too afraid to look back. David was dreadfully upset. It would take him weeks to adjust to no Flymo. She would crowd his thoughts so much that his schoolwork would suffer and dreams about her would disturb his sleep. Yet he was the more fortunate one. He had a mum and dad who loved him and soon Flymo would be replaced by a new pet in a new place. Life was to be more disastrous for her than even she could imagine.

Two hours later, a fat little man in some tatty clothes came to the hutch with David's dad.

"Roight. Let's 'ave she then."

Flymo panicked as she was grabbed roughly by the throat, yanked forwards and had a strong arm clamped round her body. She could not honk and her wings were too tightly pinioned to her side to flap. She looked pathetic as all she could do was wave her webbed feet uselessly in the air. She was harshly forced into a cardboard box and held down while the top was secured. She scratched, flapped, pecked and honked in the tight space but could not do anything about it. In her terror she messed everywhere.

"Cor! Them allus stink like that when 'em scared. Good thing 'er's gowin' in the back."

For a second, Flymo felt herself and her wrapping fly through the air and then stop with a painful jolt. Instantly it brought back nightmare memories of her experience when David launched her onto the concrete. There was a bang as most of the light disappeared, and then the noise and shaking began. There was some kind of movement too.

Very slowly she calmed down. It was a very traumatic experience but apart from a growing sense of sickness, nothing seemed to be getting worse. She tried to turn her thoughts to something else.

How about some maths? That was not as silly as it sounds. Geese are brilliant mathematicians in their own way. They can navigate hundreds of miles using the sun, magnetic fields and senses unknown to man. They pick the best compromise between speed and saving energy. They know how to adjust their wing beats to varying conditions, whether harder or softer, bigger or smaller or just to glide for a bit. They know what altitude to fly at. They can even gauge whether they have taken on board enough fuel for the journey, without drawing too much on their fat reserves. They understood applied mathematics long before Pythagoras, Archimedes or Newton were on the scene.

Flymo counted her heartbeats.

"Down to 120 from 160. That's a 25% drop and still falling. This box measures 18"x12"x12". I therefore have 1½ cubic feet in which to move. That's tight. I'm cramped and my muscles are starting to hurt. There's a build up of lactic acid. (You will see she knew a lot of chemistry too.) I must breathe more slowly. The holes in the box are only just big enough. It feels like we're travelling at 35 m.p.h. in a westerly direction ..."

So her thoughts went on and it calmed her beautifully, until the van stopped.

29

The door opened and the box was lifted out. As it was being opened Flymo quickened. She could hear the honking of other geese. She stretched her wings as she escaped from the box and flapped hard. Running fast to get away from her captor, she was surprised to find herself airborne. She had never done that before. She did not get far off the ground and soon came down again. She had landed in her new home.

The words came back to her.

"... a proper house and a large area to roam around on. It'll be more natural for her ..."

Nothing could be further from the truth. The "proper house" was a derelict old wooden shed. It needed a new roof. The floor was a mixture of muck and mud. The "large area to roam around in" was ten foot by twenty. It was just mud, except where some nettles defied the occupants to nibble them. A few dishes, which had contained rolled barley, were all that remained of any natural food. Flymo stood shaking nervously as the other geese advanced on her. They were all bigger than her. The ones in front lowered their heads and hissed threateningly.

"David!" her heart sobbed. "I want to come home!"

5. *Misery*

A big grey gander crept round Flymo, head lowered, feathers ruffled to appear large and threatening. He succeeded.

A.P.

"He must be over fifteen pounds in weight. That makes him approximately 53.5% heavier than me ..."

Maths failed to soothe Flymo's nerves. She was scared. She had good reason to be so. She had never mixed with her own kind before. They did not seem as friendly as humans. She was right. These ones were not.

The grey gander drawled with an American accent. "Well looky here now," he said as he sized her up. "Who are you?"

Flymo was so fearful, her voice was faint and appealing. "My name's Fl... Fl..F..."

"Is that so? Well, Miss Fluff-Fluff or whatever ya call yaself, I'm Aggro and this is why I'm called it!"

Instantly he pecked her hard across the cheek. Flymo squealed with pain. Immediately another large grey gander pecked her hard across the neck and shook her. A goose peck is hard to describe to someone who has never felt it. The nearest experience is to imagine being grabbed by an enormous pair of pliers and pulled. The bruise it leaves, together with the soreness, show how painful such an attack is. Flymo was well protected by feathers but she still felt the sharp pain. Still squealing she tried to back away, fending off the attack with her wings. These did not feel the bites so much. She turned and fled into a corner of the muddy pen. The second gander followed her in and carried on some more. He clearly enjoyed it but fortunately for Flymo his enjoyment was short-lived.

"Oi! Pack it en!"

A hard thrown stone from Flymo's new owner hit her attacker on the web of his foot. He jumped, or rather hopped, back, flapping to balance as best he could. He limped away but in between hurtful honks he threatened Flymo.

"I'll git ya for this. Me an' Aggro don't tolerate no nonsense from the likes of tatty wimps like yesel'."

32

"At-a-boy, Hassle! Ya done told her well and good," agreed Aggro.

Flymo was quaking in the corner. The journey had left her shaken. The physical attack had been worse. What hurt her most though was the mental strain. Why did they not like her? How had she offended them? What would she have to face next? How could she survive as a prisoner in this stinking muddy patch? Worse was to come.

In a very short time, all the geese were herded into the hovel of a shed. Flymo did not know where to go. Every bit of space seemed to belong to someone else, and she had to run the gauntlet until she found a tiny area which no one drove her from. Fortunately it was out of reach of Aggro and Hassle. She still got pecked at for no apparent reason but not so badly as by those two. She did not retaliate. She was not only scared to, but it would only invite more trouble.

That night was only the beginning. Life soon became unbearable. There was no grass to nibble at. Conditions were overcrowded, especially in the so-called shelter. Fighting occurred occasionally and bullying more often. She would regularly be chased around the dark shed, falling over other birds, who in turn would snap at her, frequently causing her to hit the walls. Aggro justified this treatment by remarking that, as she was such a tatty looking bird to begin with, it did not make much difference. She soon became muddy and was hard to tell apart from some of the others, except for her sideways pointing tail. There was not enough water to clean herself with, something important for a goose, and she was soon out of condition. It was not long before the ticks and lice spread from the other inmates to her. These sucked her blood and she had trouble replenishing it. She was usually last in the scramble, when the kitchen leftovers were thrown amongst them.

There was only one occasion when she was first, but not to the food. Shortly before Christmas it snowed. The geese did not rush out in their usual noisy haste to tell the world they had arrived on the scene. They were puzzled by the snow. They had never seen it before and it made them nervous.

"OK. Fluff-Fluff. Git aht 'n' see what it is."

"Well, I'm not sure I can. It looks so different. Where has the mud gone? The ground is higher and it's all such a bright white. It hurts my eyes and ..."

"Quit stallin' and move!" honked Aggro and pushed her out, chewing at her with his bill to emphasise the point.

Flymo jumped forwards and disappeared up to her breast into the snow. The others, finding that it did not hurt her, then worked their way out to the food before she got a look-in.

Perhaps what you have read so far about Flymo's suffering makes you think that geese fight and hurt each other a lot but this is not true. Despite their reputation, they are social creatures and like lots of company. The trouble seen when the members of the group change is simply a primitive way of working out some kind of order; the pecking order. Once it is established, there may be a lot of noise and occasional pecks to keep the hierarchy maintained but life carries on, under a recognised system of who bosses who around. There is nothing like the violence seen in a flock of chickens, where a cockerel will quite happily kill a rival, or several hens will peck another one to death. Flymo was fitting in to this system. Unfortunately for her, she had found her way straight to the bottom of the pile.

When Christmas came, things improved slightly. Some of the other occupants were grabbed unceremoniously by the throat and carried screaming away. It made more room. Pining in the corner on a cold Christmas day, Flymo overheard an older goose explaining what had happened. "Every year, when the days are at their shortest, people all over the country take a domestic bird, especially a plump one, and eat it."

To a vegetarian like Flymo, eating meat was an awful thought. To eat a goose was simply shocking! Now she understood what David's dad had meant when he said that the others would soon be needed for Christmas. She shuddered as she realised what a fate she had missed. Thank goodness she had been so badly fed. Those greedy ones who had always got to the food first, and had eaten more than their share, were the ones who had been taken and even now were being ... No. She could not bear to think of it. She would simply remember in future that greed has a price, and it might be better not to think any further. Meanwhile the older bird was continuing.

"We were some of the earliest animals, and certainly the most important ones, that people kept. Ten thousand years ago, as the ice which covered most of the world was melting, we were among the first pioneering creatures to move into the newly exposed lands of the north. Men followed after us. Though we often fought hard, they regularly plundered our nests for eggs to eat."

Flymo could not believe it. Eggs to eat? They not only ate geese but destroyed defenceless unborn creatures for their greed? Humans were awful! It would not surprise her if they did not go round killing each other after all she had heard! She listened more intently. This was revealing.

"They soon discovered that newly hatched goslings and those just coming out of their shells could become quite tame so they kept them to live amongst them. When I say tame, by the way, I do not mean it in the way that we see other so-called animals used as pathetic fools. Some of them have been reduced to running after sticks, for the sole purpose of bringing them back so that they can run after them again.

"They even do undignified things like lying on their backs while those humans seem to get some pleasure from rubbing their tummies! No, we're not tame in that sense. We have our pride and our dignity!"

There were murmurs of approval from the rest of the flock. Quite so. No goose would ever allow itself to be used like that! As the chorus of voices died down the old goose carried on.

"Over hundreds of years the humans selected which of us should be allowed to have goslings and so produced only the best kind of goose. We're very select, you see, or else we shouldn't be here, though I can't understand how some of us still exist." She glanced across at Flymo.

"However, to continue. The domestic, or as we call ourselves, the 'super' goose became much bigger and stronger than the wild goose and many of us, myself included of course, have a pedigree. I come from a very significant strain called the 'West of England.' Luigi, here is a Roman. He should be all white but he doesn't bath often enough."

There were peals of laughter from some of the group, but the sensible ones kept quiet. Luigi had a short fuse and hurt people who irritated him.

"Whafor you are a laughing at uh? I smasha ya beak in! Is na mia fault we donna ge' enough water! Why, we Romans is inventa the bath! Justa south of 'ere isa 'ole town is name after the bath we ava install!"

"Quite, quite. Now please sit down, Luigi ..."

"An another thingi, we maka da best guards da greatest empire 'ave ever sin, so. We sava da big city froma da ancient French."

"Yes, I'm quite sure that the myth may contain some truth, now ..."

"Ana thasa not all! Whafor you are a ... Mamma mia! ...You taka youse wings offa me!"

"I ain't takin' no wings offa ya. Jes' siddan an' shudup like the lady says afore I rams ya hid dan ya gizzard, pardner!"

"Yes, well ...er ... quite... em... thank you Aggro for your kind words. It's always nice to hear from a gentleman from across the water."

"I'm an American Buff, lady, and I'd be mighty obliged if ya din' call me an' my brother Hassle gen'lemen 'cause we ain't, are we, Fluff-Fluff?"

Flymo was shocked to find herself the centre of attention. "Well I ... oh dear!"

"Jus' what kinda answer is that supposed ta be? What kinda goose are ya anyway? Why d'ya talk so like ya's singin'? Where's ya from?"

"I'm a Brecon Buff, from Wales, look you. We all speak more normal over there."

38

"Well, how come ya ain't called Buff-Buff? An' that ain't all. How come ya's brown if ya's meant to be buff like me?"

"Truth to tell my name's Flymo. I was given it at the place where I used to live. It was a lovely place with a dry shelter and lots of food. There was grass everywhere, though they had a machine to eat it instead of animals. Well, when I say they had a machine to eat the grass instead of animals, I mean it didn't normally eat animals and then grass at other times ...you see ...that is ...well, it eats grass instead of us eating it, if you understand me."

"'Fraid I cain't rightly say I does."

Aggro's lack of grass in his own diet was getting at him.

"Is that why we ain't got no grass here? Ya mean some machine critter munched it all before we arrived? Ah trash! Who ever heard of a machine gittin' hungreh? Don't make no sense to me, an' ya still ain't ansa'ed ma quishchin. If ya's a buff, how comes ya's brown? Ya ain't nothin' like me."

"You're not buff, you're grey. Perhaps you're more of a mongrel?"

A gasp went up among the assembled group. Flymo had insulted Aggro's pride, by telling the truth before thinking what the consequences would be. It amounted to a challenge to someone higher up the pecking order.

"I don' take that from nobody!" screamed the brash overweight bully.

In a second the lecture ceased as Aggro unleashed his temper on Flymo. All the other geese got out the way quickly except for Luigi, who was still thinking up a retort to Aggro's earlier abuse, when the same bird ran straight across him, banging his head down in the mud with his heavy foot.

That set off a brief argument, in which time, much to Flymo's relief, she got forgotten.

Eventually, amongst some unintelligible Latin mutterings from Luigi, the lecture continued.

"Soon we were beginning to be appreciated for the superb creatures we are."

Murmurs of approval came from the audience, except for Luigi who was still mumbling to himself.

"Pictures of us were to be found on walls of buildings in ancient Egypt, at least four thousand years before the present. In Rome, as Luigi has told us, geese were kept as sacred animals. In Wales - that's a place just left of Gloucester - Druids, special men who ruled the place, refused to eat us."

"At least I come from a country where humans are normal and have the right attitudes," thought Flymo.

"Regrettably, for the last two thousand years or so humans have betrayed us. No longer have we commanded the respect we deserve, despite their dependence on us. They needed us for so many things. We were the most efficient grazers. From us they collected the largest eggs of any domestic bird, eggs which made the fluffiest of omelettes. They used our flesh for food when the grass died down for the winter. Millions of us were eaten at Christmas for several hundreds of years. Our grease was excellent for cooking and much else. Our down feathers become part of their bedclothes to keep them warm, while our quill feathers made one of the best natural pens they ever wrote with. We were so important that whole markets and fairs were devoted to us. They would paint our feet with tar to protect them and make us walk to these markets, sometimes up to eighty miles.

"Now, sadly, our numbers have dropped from millions to thousands, and many stories and sayings about us are unknown to most people. We are a joke and despised by many of them. We might just as well be extinct, like our wild ancestors now are."

This talk was having a mixed effect on the hearers. Some were feeling sick at the descriptions of how the different bits of them were dismembered and used. Some felt proud at how important they had once been. Others felt angry at the way they had been treated. Flymo felt unhappier than ever. Other geese treated her badly. Humans sounded even worse.

6. The Fully Automatic Self-Fuelling Multipurpose Weedkilling Lawnmowers

"Well, the parrots were very entertaining but do tell me more about your goose," said James.

"Snowflake? Yes, 'er's quoite a character. Us got she from a fellow as worked at the old airfield, at Aston Down. 'Er were the only goose in the country with her own landing strip and runway! Him were moving 'owse so us had she yur."

"She could be the answer to our problem. You see we've got a great stretch of lawn that's taking over the garden. If grass is the staple diet of a goose, one of them could be used to keep it down. Mind you, I'm a bit concerned about the children. Geese can hurt can't they?"

"A lat of things can 'urt. Woi single owt a goose? If 'em woz zo daindros 'ow did children survoive in olden days when geese was as common in every 'ows'old as what pets is today?"

That was a good point. James went into the library in Gloucester after school the next day. He consulted some books on smallholdings, keeping domestic fowl and similar subjects.

The general books on farm animals had little to say about geese. In days gone by, they had fed on grass and when that died they were fattened up by releasing them into the recently harvested cereal fields. They did a good job of clearing up the remains that got dropped. With their natural food all gone, they were then slaughtered just in time for the Michaelmas feast in September. However, it was different now. It was not just that the Michaelmas fairs and celebrations had more or less died out. It appeared that, because they were little changed from their wild ancestors, they were not commercially viable.

In an age when farming is geared to profit and efficiency the humble goose is a non-starter. She is doing well if the number of eggs she lays in a year reaches double figures. She cannot hope to compete with a battery hen who can manage hundreds in that time. Similarly, big heavy birds though they are, geese cannot put on weight like chickens or turkeys do in time for Christmas, not unless they are stuffed full of expensive feeds. Even then much of their weight is fat, not meat.

The decline of the British goose is all too obvious today. How many hen's eggs have you eaten? How many goose eggs have you had? Again, how many chickens and turkeys have you had at Christmas? How does that compare with the number of geese you have eaten? In this day and age, they have become mere relics, kept by very few.

James put the books back. He had only been reading an hour but already his mind was fuddled. He was tired and anything, even a goose, was welcome if it cut down on all he had to do. Later that week, an advertisement appeared in the local paper:

Wanted: good natured goo(ee)se for light lawn-mowing duties. Phone: 12345

The response was interesting. One person 'phoned up to say they would like the goo(ee)se. Emma pointed out that it was "wanted" and not "for sale". Another person 'phoned to say they had introduced an extra goose to their gander but his original mate was not having it and had started bullying the new one. Would James like to give the unhappy bird a new home? James would have said "Yes", but he had just accepted an offer from a fellow with a smallholding near Gloucester, who had started to real- ise that he had too many in his flock. James was very busy with schoolwork so he could not take up the small- holder's offer straight away. It was arranged that they would be picked up in the New Year when James had found the time and the energy to make their home.

So it was to Flymo's delight that one day, in early Spring, a minibus turned up and Aggro and Hassle were unceremoniously bundled off to a new locality. They complained long and loud but changed their minds when they saw their new home.

"Man! How d'ya like this? Oodles of grass just beginning to sprout up! Wow! That tastes real good. I ain't had it for so long that I'd plumb forgotten what this stuff was like. Why I ain't tasted grub like this since the day the boss left the gate open and we all done got ourselves into his vegetable patch. Look at this! It's even got dandelions, buttercups and other goodies! Hey! This patch is clover! It's far out, man!"

They were very taken with the living accommodation too. It looked a bit like a bus shelter. It was an old wooden structure which a previous owner of the garden had used to keep his horse in. It now had a pair of doors made from two old fencing panels. Inside was a layer of straw with an attractive scent (to a goose). On a wide platform a few feet up were half a dozen bales of spare straw. The outside was newly creosoted and looked very attractive (to a human). A chain link fence ran around it, to provide a pen when people wanted to use the garden. Inside the penned area an old cast iron bath, still with mixer tap and shower fitting attached, had been sunk into the ground to make a pond for swimming in.

"Yahee!" screeched Hassle as he slid in. "This sure do beat the old tub on the smallholding. Hmm. Man. Pass the shower gel and turn on the spray! Make sure there's enough warm water. Have ya seen the bath salts Aggro?"

"Hold on there bathmate. I'm still looking for the soap!"

So the conversation went on. It was pure fantasy. No plumbing was connected up.

"Hey! What's goin' on? The water's gone AWOL! Hassle ya nitwit! Ya dang gone and pulled the plug out!"

"Hang it, Aggro! I jes' wanted to know what was on the end of this chain thing!"

After half an hour of struggling to climb up the enamelled sides of the now empty bath, the pair were eventually found and rescued by James. That night they settled very happily into the straw.

"Yessir. We're gonna do jes' fine here. I wonder how lil' ol' Flymo's getting on without us to care for her?"

Flymo was not too happy. For the next three months Luigi took over as the number one bully. She wished she could be elsewhere.

Another member of her species, who had moved elsewhere but who was just as unhappy, was Eric. During his first winter in Britain, he and his family had eked out a living on the poor vegetation found along the shores. Their fat, aided by their feathers, kept them insulated from the cold and it also provided a store to supplement their limited diet. Later, instinct and the influence of the older birds led him to make the return journey back to Iceland. His mother had become less interested in him lately and her time and attention had become concentrated more and more on a new gander. Eric was jealous and had threatened this new intruder. He had only had to hiss a couple of times before the adult bird made him suffer for it. To add insult to injury, Eric's mother actually sided with the stranger. The final upset came when he was driven off by her and his newly acquired stepfather for the last time.

It was a miserable existence. One of these days he would find a mate of his own, he decided. He would show his mum and stepfather how to look after children! However he was too young for that now. He found himself on the edge of the colony and its social life but the experience would not be wasted. With little else to do while others were raising families, he would feed to his heart's content and became a strong, woll built young gander. He would even make himself useful occasionally by setting off the hue and cry if he noticed any potential marauders around. As winter reapproached he would be keen and able to set off on the long flight once more.

7. Who's Boss?

During May life seemed to pick up for Flymo. Two good things happened as far as she was concerned.

The first was that just when Luigi had become unbearable, he too had been dragged off kicking, flapping and screaming in the blue minibus. The reason was simple. Aggro and Hassle were finding the grass too much to eat that year. The winter had been unusually mild and the spring wet and warm. This meant that the grass had not stopped growing all winter and now it was growing at an even faster rate. The two ganders could not keep pace with it so another one was bought.

The other good thing was that Flymo managed to lay an egg of her own. It surprised her at first and left her feeling a little bit queasy but she soon forgot about that. Three days later she recognised the symptoms arriving and so was less surprised to produce another egg. Her interest in her achievement started to grow with the fourth egg, and by the time the sixth one appeared she was sitting constantly on the clutch. In all she produced seven. They were infertile, and every night she left them to go cold when she retired to the hut. Despite being a brilliant mathematician, Flymo was no biologist. She did not understand that the eggs would not hatch. It did provide her with a new instinct though. If any creature came near her, she hissed and threatened. Her status went up amongst the flock. She would see off the strongest bird and think nothing of pecking them if she felt her treasure was at risk. Life actually felt good. She was important and respected. If only it had lasted. Events in the Stewarts' garden prevented it.

The family had hoped for some eggs as a spin-off from the goose enterprise but that had not occurred. Neither James nor the owner of the smallholding had been any good at telling the difference between geese and ganders so James had ended up with two males instead of two females.

All had gone well at first. Then the mating season arrived. Both the birds were getting aggressive. James was sitting in the garden stroking Aggro when Hassle got jealous and seized him by the thigh. It was most unexpected and the shock caused James to leap to his feet, with Hassle still attached to him. Furious, James hit Hassle several times across the head till he let go. Aggro immediately launched in on Hassle's side. James' left hand was firmly in the vice of Aggro's bill when Hassle seized his thigh in exactly the same place again. Hassle, angry at being hit by James, took this opportunity to hit him back with his wings. James retreated, only to trip on the bath taps and keel over into the murky depths. Aggro was impressed with the effect of Hassle's wings, so he added his own to the punishment. He had the advantage that his victim had conveniently fallen over so it was easy to smack him in the face.

James had no recollection of how he got out of the bath, let alone the garden, nor how he managed to shut himself on the other side of the gate, just out of reach of the long

necks which were poking through and still trying to reach him in their rage. Daniel came out to see what all the excitement was about.

"Crumbs! What happened to you, Dad? You look like you've just been in a battle!"

"Nothing as mild as that," moaned James.

His face was swelling by the minute where Aggro had beaten him. His eye was watering. He had a bill-shaped bruise on his hand. The thigh which had been mauled twice was extremely tender. Such clothing as had not been torn by claws and bills was well and truly wet and muddy.

"I thought they were supposed to be mild natured vegetarians! They're blinking man eaters! What came over them? One minute I was happily stroking one and the next they both sentenced me to death! How am I going to get my book back? Oh help! They've got the gate open! Run for your life!"

Father and son did not have to escape far before an unexpected form of help appeared. Squire, the pet border collie, proved his stock handling talents with something other than sheep. He had managed to remain aloof from the action so far but he objected to Aggro grabbing his tail. Instantly, he seized Aggro by the throat and forced his head to the ground. Still holding the front end down, he climbed on the brute's back and held the wings flat out with his front legs, aided by the weight of his body. Splayed out like this, Aggro was helpless. Hassle did not wait to see if Squire could do that sort of thing to both of them at the same time, but turned and fled, complaining, back into the garden.

Squire could have killed Aggro then and there. He'd regularly caught and dealt instant death to rabbits, pigeons and pheasants, yet generations of border collies had been bred to know the difference between wild animals and those specially kept by people. As it was, all Daniel had to do was count ten, say "Break", and award the match to Squire, who promptly released his opponent. Aggro ran squealing to Hassle for comfort.

"Well Hassle, fine help ya bin when I needed ya!"

"Thanks for the appreciation Aggro. I was really rootin' for ya."

"Ya yellah bellied chicken!"

"You got that wrong. I ain't a yellah bellied chicken. I'm a grey bellied goose, same as you. Anyhow, what's the colour of ma stomach got to do with it?"

"Ah stash it. Mebbe we oughta back off. Here comes that mutt and his man agin."

James was advancing back down the garden to retrieve his book, making sure he kept the dog between himself and the ganders. He withdrew on recovering his objective, still keeping the dog between him and his new enemy. The situation was ridiculous. Not a single member of the family could get in or out of the garden, at least not without the dog! None of the text books had anything to say about this. In desperation James telephoned Folly Farm at Bourton-on-the-Water. Here was one of the world's best breeding centres for domestic and wild fowl. What they did not know about geese, nobody else was likely to.

"Oh that's no problem," came the voice at the other end of the line. "It sounds like you've got two ganders. At this time of year they get very protective about other geese. What happened was that when you stroked one, the other took it as an attack on a goose who needed his protection. Ganders still believe in chivalry so he came to the rescue of a companion in distress and promptly launched himself at you. When you hit him, it was the other one's turn to believe that you were attacking a needy friend. As a result they both went for you - to protect each other. Follow me? Simple bird psychology!"

"You mean it was twice as bad as if I'd threatened a goose during the mating season while her gander was about?"

"Something like that."

"The question remains, though. What can I do about it? If I introduce a couple of proper real genuine lady type geese, will they sort themselves out?"

"Doubtful. They'll probably think they have even more ladies to protect and get even worse!"

"Is there anything else I can do?"

"Not a lot I'm afraid. Can you survive till you next need a Christmas dinner? They'll probably settle down before then anyway. The mating season only lasts a couple of months or so."

"I can't wait. At present we can only get into the garden armed with a stick or a dog. We can't even hang out the washing!"

"A stick will only rile them more. Be brave, grab them by the throat and hold them until they surrender. Let them go and they'll back off till the next time. Eventually they'll get the message and there won't be a next time."

"How will I know when they've surrendered?"

"Let go and if they back off you've won."

"What if they don't accept that I've won?"

"You'll know that because they'll go for you again. Not to worry though. Just grab them by the throat again. You'll win eventually!"

"Well, thanks for your help. I must rush. It now sounds like there has been another disaster outside. Thanks again"

"You're welcome. Best of luck!"

Outside James found there had been another crisis. The source of the shouting and crying was little Fiona and her friend. They came running to him, very distressed.

"Daddy! The gooses have comed into the paddling pool and tried to bited us!"

Sure enough, Aggro and Hassle were swimming around the children's inflatable paddling pool, with very smug looks on their faces. James was cross that they had got through the gate and upset the children. Wasn't their own bit of garden big enough? Wasn't their own bath satisfactory? Right! Here was a chance to put the expert's advice into action!

The family were delighted to find that it worked, even for the children. Soon the dog was redundant. James was not convinced, meanwhile, that some gentle ladylike influence would not work. He needed an extra lawnmower, so back to Flymo's new home he went.

Luigi had been selected as arrival number three because he was so small. Tho smallholder had reasoned that geese were smaller than ganders so Luigi must be a goose. It did not take long for the family to realise that this was not so. Still no eggs appeared. The grass was continuing to win the battle too, so James was yet again back at the smallholding.

"Can you guarantee that the one I get this time will really, truly, honestly and genuinely be a goose, and not a gander, beyond any possible shadow of a doubt?"

"No trouble. Look at the tatty - I min - 'taters. Jos' in front of them there's a foin yong one as 'as bin sittin' on a nest of eggs for seven weeks. Moss' be a goose eh?"

Flymo went berserk. She fought both men with her bill, wings and claws. Every ounce of strength in her body went into the struggle, but it was no good. She found herself in a box again. Her mind was screaming for her nest of eggs and there was nothing she could do. She could not believe it was happening. Surely it could not get any worse.

It could and did. When the tortured goose was released from her box, she shook her dizzy head and tried to focus her eyes. She heard before she saw.

"Landsakes! Jes' looky here, nah! We's got oursel's a new companion!"

"Isa fantastico! Yousa gonna regret acomin' 'ere Flymo!"

8. Humiliation

The family could not believe the hostile reaction the three residents gave Flymo. They all went for her at once. Having been removed from her precious clutch of eggs, she reverted to her old self. She was too demoralised to do anything about it.

"Bully me!" seemed to be written across her face.

The family found it necessary to make a temporary barrier in the shed to protect poor Flymo on one side from the three on the other side.

" I giss it's jest gonna be like old times!" chuckled Aggro.

"Isa exactly right! They gotta leta yous out tomorrow and then we'sa gonna 'ave some sport, eh boys?"

"Sure thing! You hear that Flymo?"

Flymo did. It was hardly possible to ignore it; but she did not care any more. Her misery at the loss of her eggs and status was so bad that the ganders' threats did not make a lot of difference. Everything about her circumstances seemed beyond her control, and she felt resigned to whatever happened.

The bully boys found that bullying a victim that does not react becomes boring. They soon stopped hurting her as a regular event. It made no change to her mental state. She ate hardly any of the much improved diet on offer.

She did not take advantage of the regularly replenished clean water to spruce herself up. Her condition deteriorated slowly.

Several things stopped her going downhill too fast. Her poor health meant she was taken to the vet and various treatments slowed down her rate of decline. Despite her earlier diet, she still possessed reasonable reserves of fat, on which she lived. Added to that, an animal that just sits does not burn up its energy store very fast. Moreover, she was young. She had yet to grow naturally frail.

All this helped her through the following winter, which was fortunately another mild one. Surprisingly too, for a creature in such a weak mental and bodily condition, she actually started laying eggs again. She did not get a chance to become broody this time, for they were instantly removed to make omelettes. However, it did seem to mark a turning point. The family started to feel appreciative towards her. She began to realise that her regular visits to the vet were out of concern for her. Then one evening, as she returned to her little section of the shed she had a pleasant surprise.

There were half a dozen eggs. They were smaller than the ones she laid but bigger than the ones a hen would lay. She was puzzled. She had not produced them. Was there another bird on the scene? Had it decided to come and live in her compartment? She waited but the door was shut without anyone appearing. She decided to ignore them and left them the next morning as she went out into the garden.

"It does not seem to have worked, Dad. The eggs are in the same position and they're cold."

"Never mind. Leave them alone for now. It could take a bit of time."

Flymo was still puzzled. What were they talking about?

It was an idea that James had had when he was travelling to work near Cranham. There was a sign saying:

They could do with some, to supplement Flymo's. He pulled the motor bike up into the lay-by and approached the farmhouse. Eight lanky black birds waddled away, quacking.

"What funny things! They look like a cross between a duck and a penguin!" he thought.

"Can oi yelp you?"

"Er, yes. I'd like a dozen eggs please. By the way, what sort are those ducks?"

"Them as is black with the green sort of sheen? They'm a black variety of Indian Ronner. Us calls 'em penguin docks 'coz of the way 'em wolks and stands oproit. Us 'ave troid to breed 'em bot 'er won't sit on 'er eggs."

That reminded James of Flymo, when they had had the opposite problem, trying to get her off her eggs.

"I wonder ..."

"That'll be a powend please."

"What? Oh yes. Em, here we are. I was wondering. Could you sell me say half a dozen of those duck eggs? I assume they're fertile? I was thinking that if I put them under a broody goose they might hatch. Even if they didn't it might solve a problem. She's almost a psychological case. It's as if she saw no point in living. Simply sitting on some eggs might give her a purpose in life, some reason for living after all."

"Well tha's a rum un. Oi've never 'urd of a goose 'achen docks' eggs afore! Oi can't see it 'appnin' mesel', bot you never know. Tell you what. Oi'll give you the eggs loik if you can return me 'alf the docklin's if it works. 'Ow's 'at?"

"Smashing idea! Oh! Sorry. Perhaps that wasn't a good adjective to use about eggs! Never mind. Let's have them then and we'll give it a go."

So that's how Flymo found the eggs in her straw. Although she did not return to them during the day, they were very much on her mind. An instinct was growing on her. That night as she was shut in she investigated them. She then tried spreading herself over them. They felt a funny size, but it was, nevertheless, not uncomfortable. It even felt a bit satisfying. She stood up to look at them. She shuffled them around a bit, turned them over and settled down again. Yes. That felt good. Quite nice really. If only they were hers. Well? Why shouldn't they be? After all, she was sitting on them. Whose else could they be? Flymo was getting what they call "broody".

In the morning she did not come out when the doors were opened and the noisy trio reawoke the neighbourhood.

"Dad! She's stayed put! I've tried to move her but she's getting quite stroppy."

"OK. Let's leave her for now and see what happens."

Flymo stayed put for a time until it seemed that everyone, human, goose or otherwise, had moved off. Happy though she was to remain there, she felt the need to move out and have a drink.

"Hey boize. Looka what weeza got coming here! Whasa matter wiz youse? You lika your sleep too much uh?"

Flymo ignored Luigi and had a long draw on the water. She lifted her head to drain it gently down her throat. It tasted and felt fresh. She did it again. She felt clean inside but she began to notice her plumage. In all honesty, it looked disgusting. No self-respecting bird would look like that. Flymo began to feel more self-respecting and decided to do something about it. She burrowed her head under the water and shook it around.

 That felt nice. She did it again, then a third time. Then she shook her head and scattered the water over her back. This was more like it. How could she have neglected herself so much? With a feeling of

pride Flymo wet her head again and rubbed it all over her back. She stretched her wings out over their full three feet of span and gave a few good beats. Hmm. They needed attention and they got it as she preened under them with her wet bill.

Aggro, Hassle and Luigi stared speechlessly. What had come over her?

" I giss it must be somethin' in the shed. Le's go 'long an' take us a lil' mosey 'round."

Hassle had made a good guess for once. The three stared.

"Ain't no way she coulda laid all them in such a short time."

"Nope. I reckon not. Or mebee she did an' tha's why they come out so small, Aggro."

"Donna you talka so stupido! Isa no possible."

"OK. So how's she done it? Six eggs jus' like that?"

"I'ma no gonna explain, but maybe if I'sa gonna go for a walk all over them I donna 'ave to explain 'cos she donna 'ave no more."

"That sure do sound like a swell idea. Me first."

Aggro was first, but not to stamp on the eggs. He was the first to experience the full force of Flymo's maternal protection. Yesterday's pathetic little wimp had been transformed into a terror to anyone who approached the clutch. Like most bullies, these three were cowards under the surface. They did not remain around long. It was the pattern for the next four weeks. Flymo rarely left the nest, but when she did she ruled the roost. The three ganders kept their distance. It was even possible to remove the partition between them and her. Then the great event happened.

Four of the eggs hatched over two days. The ganders knew something was up but could not get near enough to find out. However, Flymo could not stay put forever and soon she appeared in the garden with her foster children. If geese could blush she would have done so. Her offspring were pitch black and waddled like penguins. She could not believe it, let alone understand it. Neither could the ganders.

Luigi just stood there shaking help-lessly with mirth. Aggro and Hassle could hardly stand up they were so full of laughter.

"Hey! Who's their dad? A sunburnt penguin?"

"Dad ain't got nothin' to do with it. She kept them eggs so hot she done gone burnt them!"

The ridicule continued with much laughter and rude remarks. Flymo coped with it and certainly did not let anyone near her brood. They might be odd but they were hers and she would protect them from anything. Sadly though, they did not help her image. She was rapidly becoming the joke of the neighbourhood. The loud-mouthed Aggro soon made sure that not only the domestic animals but the wild ones knew about it as well, and many of them came to look and laugh.

One of them who heard the news had a fierce reputation and was generally feared by all the others. This was a contrast, for his own name was Fearless and it suited him. He had killed most other kinds of animals. Horses and cows were too big and he just ignored them and treated them with contempt. He had fought with individual dogs and had hurt them more than they hurt him. He would avoid packs of them but would happily sit on a wall above them, just high enough to be safe, but aggravating them by his unreachable presence. He decided to see for himself what this freak occurrence was, and perhaps even increase his reputation by depriving other spectators of it.

Flymo had lost all patience and was getting hysterical with her children. They were perpetually in and out of the bath. They kept their heads under the water for far too long. She was willing to excuse this behaviour, but nothing could excuse their disgusting eating habits. They were eating woodlice! She had caught one of them trying to swallow a large snail and yet another one had just devoured a massive worm! Being a vegetarian, the sight made her feel sick.

"Stop it! Stop it! You're making me ill! Why can't you eat grass and other sensible vegetables like any normal geese? Why can't you be the proper colour and shape and walk properly too?"

She would have ranted and raved a lot more, but her whole body suddenly froze. It was ominously quiet. The ganders were gaping in her direction. Sitting casually on the wall above her, the face leered down. His eyes seemed to pierce and paralyse her. What was it? She had never before seen a fox. His stare seemed to burn straight through to her petrified heart. She stood almost hypnotised. She wanted to escape but could not move. The ducklings began to crowd underneath her, nervously. Before Flymo's numb mind could react, Fearless had jumped down, barged her aside, and seized one of the ducklings. The jolt shook Flymo and the others into noisy action, but Fearless was already back up on the wall with the limp little black body hanging from his mouth. He stared down at the excited animals below with indifference. He ignored their hisses and screams, merely sitting and watching. They could not reach him and he was not in the mood to deal with large angry ganders. Maybe if he was hungry he would risk it, but why bother taking on unnecessary trouble now? He had a tasty morsel and was content with that. Fearless lowered the remains of Flymo's precious child onto the wall.

"Thanks for the snack. I'll be back for you next time, Tatty! Stay around and I won't disappoint you. I've never broken a promise yet!"

Again his eyes seemed to drive straight through Flymo. Fearless picked up the corpse and waved its pathetic form contemptuously at her, before he walked slowly along the wall and slipped lightly down into a neighbour's garden.

9. *Changes for Many*

The loss of the duckling was soon noticed by the children. Emma decided it would be better to give the remaining three back to the farm they came from, before the cat, or whatever had taken the first one, came back for the rest. It was sad for the family but it was devastating for Flymo. It was bad enough to lose your eggs but to see your hatchling killed in front of you and then have the rest taken away was too much. She sank to an all-time low. She had nothing to live for and began pining away again. It was made worse by the certain knowledge that Fearless had singled her out to kill. She could tell he meant it. She could not even find satisfaction in a quadratic equation. What could she do?

In despair, the answer came. She would defy him! That was it! She would defy him! Why was he intent on her destruction? Merely to make a meal of her? Of course not. Just as important, it was to boost his ego. Well she would deny him such satisfaction! Flymo had the sense to realise that she could not avoid her death sooner or later. After all, it's a characteristic of all living things. One day they stop being alive. No, Flymo could not avoid her death but she could influence how she died. It did not have to be at the jaws of Fearless. He could not kill her if she was dead already! That was it. She would let this broken-heart end it all, so that he could never have the privilege of boasting that he had vanquished her. She would end up like Hassle. That too was a sad story. He had died that day.

66

He had found his way into the vegetable patch. Unlike the others he had not gone for the cabbages and lettuces. He started chewing at the rhubarb instead. It's hard to understand why Hassle took to the poisonous, bitter leaves. Sadly, horrible things can become an addiction. When the four raiders were driven out by a furious James, demanding to know who had left the gate open, Hassle staggered out last, feeling very upset in the tummy. He spent the rest of the day both hating and craving more rhubarb leaves. During the night he had cramps in his muscles and felt that the only relief would be to eat more rhubarb. By morning it was irresistible. He struggled and fought his way under the wire fence until he could make his way through and devour as much as he could. He ruined five whole plants before he was found by James, who soon forgot his fury when he saw the state of his pet. Gently, he stood the gander up but it collapsed straight away. Carefully, James picked up all fifteen pounds weight of Hassle plus rhubarb and carried him into the shed. On the way, Aggro pecked him. "Hey you! Leave ma pal alone will ya? Whadda ya thin' ya doin' with him?"

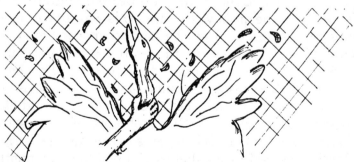

James' fury reawoke. He dropped Hassle and seized Aggro by the throat. He lifted him off the ground and shook his fat form from side to side. So great was his grip that Aggro's brain began to be starved of blood and oxygen. The world seemed to go blue as James finally vented his anger by throwing him up against the shed.

"That's one way of opening a door," thought Flymo. "Now if force equals mass times acceleration, or deceleration in Aggro's case, that means the impact would have been approximately 7kg. multiplied by approximately one metre per second per second ..."

James' thoughts were on a totally different subject to Flymo's. Hassle was going downhill fast. He would not eat and would not drink. His eyes were half closed and his wings hung down beside him; he did not even have the strength to tuck them away. He lasted another day like that. James managed to pour some apple juice down his unresisting gullet, and he believed Hassle must be getting better because he had eaten the cereal left in front of him. The truth was that Aggro and Luigi had robbed him. By afternoon Hassle's eyes glazed over.

James had a shock when he came down after dinner. The shed was buzzing with flies. Hassle's stiff form lay spread out across the straw. Despite their mutual dislike, James felt a deep conviction that this was all wrong and was deeply upset. Soon the four other members of the family felt the same. The flies were not upset and more and more were being attracted all the time. This had to be dealt with as soon as possible. James dug a pit as deep as he could. It was not as deep as he would have preferred, because of the problems of old cottage foundations and a rock layer so close to the surface. Hassle was laid in it. James planned to plant another fruit tree on the spot. How could he mark how deep Hassle was so he did not dig too far when planting the tree? Of course. A layer of newspaper before the soil was put on. That should do as a marker. Off he went to get an old copy of the Stroud News.

The gravedigger was puzzled when he returned with the shroud. The body had gone. At first there was no clue to the mystery until a slight movement appeared in the cypress trees. Hassle could not be alive after all, could he? On investigation James found him, still dead, lying between the paws of a guilty looking sheep-dog.

"Sorry to disappoint you, Squire," said James as he took Hassle back. "The trouble is that we wouldn't feel happy if you ate him, especially if we had to clear up the bits you couldn't manage. Anyway, if he's eaten something poisonous it wouldn't be good for you, would it?"

Squire did not see this as a problem, and watched with great disappointment as what he considered a good meal went to waste. Aggro and Luigi were not fussed. It all meant an increase in grass and scrap vegetables for their gluttonous bellies. Flymo was quite detached from it all, except that she almost envied Hassle. Death seemed to be the end.

That end nearly came at Fearless' jaws after all. Autumn came remarkably early that year, heralded by a two week cold spell. Fearless was hungry and decided the time had come to partake of the tasty dinner he had been musing upon for some time. He had left it a bit late that night and the dawn had appeared as he had tried to find a way of getting past the door of the goose shed. He had tried digging and chewing at the lock, all to no avail. Perhaps he should try the back? His mind was intent on this when he heard the sound of honking as the door opened. What had happened? Had his fiddling with the lock worked after all? Fearless was so stuck up about himself and his own achievements that the obvious answer did not occur to him. He came round the corner to the front of the shed, to see what was on offer, when he came face to face with Daniel. What was he doing there so early?

Daniel had to be up early to catch the bus at 7.45 am. now that he was at a secondary school, in Stroud. All the other pupils at Archway and the Downfield schools were making their way to the bus stop. Daniel just had time let the livestock out. That way they got an extra hour's freedom.

This change in routine had fooled Fearless. Now the two looked at each other. Daniel had never seen a fox before, let alone one so close up. He did not know what to do. Fearless, on the other hand, already had his mind at work. He

EW.

took his eyes off Daniel and focused them on Flymo. Again, Flymo felt their paralysing grip. Fearless could see it in her face. He could easily slip round the boy, grab and kill her before the lad could turn and ... and ... That's where his ideas ran out. There was no way he could drag a goose over the wall fast enough before the boy could catch him. Would the boy try? Probably not. He still looked startled. But what if he did try? Fearless could fight him off, couldn't he? What if he picked up a stick or a rock? The dry stone wall contained a whole range of sizes which he might find suitable. A previous encounter with a human had left Fearless with painful memories of a chunk of Cotswold limestone across the head. No. It was not worth the trouble. He could get away, but it would probably be without his prize.

Reluctantly he turned and jumped lightly onto the wall. He reassessed the situation and abandoned his planned menu. On descending the other side, however, he stopped to reconsider. The boy could not stand there forever, could he? He would have to move and then the great Fearless would strike. Stealthily, the hunter wandered along the wall a few yards and remounted it. Gingerly, he looked between the branches of the cypress trees. He was right. Clever old fox! His gaze followed the path to the door of the house, which was just closing.

"Stupid child. In his excitement he's run in to tell some story about how he saved his geese by driving off the great Fearless, but he hasn't realised that I'm still here! Even better, he hasn't thought to shut the birds back in for safety while he's away! Now for it."

You may by now have begun to realise that, though Fearless was intelligent, he was not as brilliant as he thought. His overestimation of himself and underestimation of others now showed. The door reopened and Daniel reappeared, with his dad's air rifle and Squire close behind. The gun had only been primed and was not loaded with a pellet but Fearless could not know that. As Daniel had suspected, Fearless had seen a rifle before and, being an experienced fox, he knew what it could do. Daniel was bearing down on him and raising the sights in his direction. He heard the sound of the air discharge and, though he felt nothing, he was more concerned that four stone of dog had overtaken the boy.

He did not hang around but returned to his earth to shelter from the cold and mourn his lost dinner. Daniel mourned too. He missed the bus and had a long walk down the valley, in order to catch a different one. Nevertheless, he had saved Flymo's life.

The rest of the day grew windier and rain began to fall heavily. After the morning's adventure it was decided to put the geese to bed early. A real storm was brewing and the predator might return. In the midst of a blustery gale, Jane shoved an indifferent goose and two objecting ganders into their shed. Aggro and Luigi were convinced it was far too early and made an issue of it very loudly, before the door could finally be shut on them.

Meanwhile, the storm was having a major effect on Eric, returning to Britain for the second time.

Even with their keen instinct for the weather, this same storm which was sweeping the north Atlantic took many of the migrating geese by surprise. The mixture of heavy rain and gale force winds drove many to seek shelter. The sea was too rough for them to land in. Many, unable to alight, were blown off course. Weaker ones perished, but Eric was not one of those. He was a powerful determined

72

creature. His presence in the leading flocks meant that
he was amongst the last ones which the storm, moving
down from the north, caught up with. Sensible birds
began to shelter from the worsening conditions at the first
opportunity. Not Eric though, he was feeling tough
enough to brave anything.

Maybe it was inexperience. Perhaps it was the strong
winds. It might have been a subtle change in the earth's
magnetism or simply that no celestial bodies could be
seen. We do not know the cause but Eric found himself
on his own. He had lost all sense of time and position yet
kept on flying, driven on by the stubbornness he had
inherited from his father. But stubbornness is no
substitute for stamina. He was getting weak. He must
be there by now? If not he would have to land now
anyway. At that moment, Eric sensed the ground was a
lot closer than he had anticipated. What was it that he

could hear? Surely it was unmistakable. Yes. There it
was again, the sound of others of his kind. He had done
it. He had arrived all by himself through the storm! He
followed the direction of the noise, got tangled in the
branches of a coppiced hazel tree and tumbled exhausted
into a cold puddle.

10. Appreciated

It was the worst storm for decades. Hurricane winds had uprooted hundreds of trees. Most of the goose shed had survived but not the roofing felt. A few tattered remains clung to the wooden roof but most of it lay scattered in sheets around the garden. The children were listening to the local radio in the unlikely hope that school would be cancelled. There had been no sign of it yet.

"Look," said a harassed Emma, "why don't you put on your duffel coats and boots and make sure all the trees in the garden are alright. Daniel, I suggest you pack your stuff for school. I assume rain doesn't stop buses so it should be along in a minute."

Still hoping that there would be no school, the girls wrapped up warmly and went outside.

"Can you let the geese out while you're there? Give them a couple of handfuls of rolled barley each and some water in the tub," James shouted after them. "While you're at it, can you clear away the roofing felt and that grey rag-like thing that seems to have blown under the tree? It won't take long."

"Why do grown-ups have to find things for us to do just as we're getting on with something else which we enjoy? It's typical. Still, the sooner we do it, the quicker we can see what the storm did. I'll do the barley and water and let them out. Pick that rag up for Daddy, Fiona, and put it in the dustbin."

The geese rushed out in their usual noisy haste to tell the world they had arrived on the scene. They made a rush for the fruit trees, because they knew that high winds brought down apples and other goodies. Yet even they were distracted by the squeal of shock that came from Fiona.

"It's alive! Help! It's moving!"

She hastily ran to her sister's side for protection.

"It's not a rag, it's a goose and it nearly comed after me!"

Cautiously, children and domestic geese gathered round the cold weak form of Eric. He had mistaken Aggro's objections to being shut in early for the call of wild geese, and it was part of the reason for his crash landing. All night he had hardly moved from the spot. Inevitable questions occurred to the watchers. Who was this stranger? Where did he come from? How had he got into the garden? When had he done so? What was going to happen now?

"We'd better get Dad."

Both children ran into the house, forgetting to remove their boots at the door. All thoughts of looking for fallen trees had gone, replaced by the excitement of the new arrival.

"Mum! Dad! Come and see what we've found in the garden! Mum! Dad! Come quickly! Now!"

"Alright! Alright! What's all the excitement? Here! Just look at the floor! Why can't you take your boots off before you come in? I spend all my time trying to keep the house clean and all you can do is ..."

"Mum! Listen! There's a goose in the garden and it's ..."

"I know there's a goose in the garden. There's three of the things if you'd only care to count. Now get your boots off at once and someone's going to have to clear up this mess ..."

"No! You don't understand! There's ..."

"I understand quite well enough. There's a mess all over the floor and someone's left the door open. We don't pay gas bills just so that we can heat up the village for everyone! Shut the door and ..."

"MUM! Listen! It's more important than that. There's a *new* goose in the garden. That big grey rag Dad thought had blown over from somewhere else turned out to be another goose. It's still alive, but only just. Come and have a look."

While the children were trying to communicate the news, Aggro and Luigi introduced themselves to Eric in the only way they knew how, a not very friendly one.

"Well stranger, ma name's Aggro, spelt K-I-L-L-E-R and I'll tell ya now that we don't take kindly to immigrant types comin' in hayer uninvited."

"Yeah!" hissed Luigi from the other side. "I'ma thinking we oughta show him jus' what wes ameaning!"

Eric hardly heard them. He was in a bad way. He had taken a hammering when he fell exhausted through the tree branches and had had to continue weathering the storm through much of the night. His layer of down feathers and fat had saved him. He was nevertheless cold, stiff and weak. He tried to react when the two troublemakers demonstrated by biting him that they were top of the pecking order, but he just didn't have the strength. Fortunately, he was reprieved by the arrival of the parents followed by the children, who drove the assailants off.

"Dear me! He is in a bad way. Perhaps we should bring him into the house."

Eric was not in agreement. He objected as best he could, but he was too feeble to make anything more than a token resistance.

"Gently does it. Don't panic and flap so, you awkward customer. We're going to try to help you."

With a beautiful blend of firmness and gentleness, James took the disabled creature in his arms and carried him into the kitchen. Tenderly he laid him on the table and observed him. Eric was spread-eagled across the table, watching everyone out of half closed eyes.

"What do we do with him now? He'll be warm in here but he'll need more than that. How about the technique we tried with Hassle?"

Eric soon experienced some humiliating handling as his throat was tipped back. However the delightful taste of warm apple juice sliding down his tongue and creating a cosy feeling inside his crop and tummy was definitely to be desired. Soon he was presented with a dish of layer's mash, made up with warm milk and accompanied by some clear water to drink. He managed a little before settling back to a doze. James lifted him down into a box lined with newspaper and placed the package next to the radiator.

Under these conditions Eric recovered very quickly. Everyone was taken by surprise when he took hours rather than days to come to, and it was clear he would not need to go to the vet as some had suspected. The other surprise was to identify, with the aid of some books and 'phone calls to the experts, that Eric was a wild greylag.

"He looks grey all over," Emma pointed out. "Which bit is his lag?"

"According to this booklet from the Wildfowl Trust at Slimbridge, it could be old English, referring to the edge of his wing. One person on the 'phone reckoned it was because they were grey birds that lag behind the others. The bigger puzzle is what this individual is doing in the Cotswolds. He's hundreds of miles south of where he should be. It's probably due to the storm, but he's travelled almost twice as far as he was supposed to."

It did not take long for this curiosity to become a problem. Within a day he had managed to get out of the box. He was not, however, friendly towards his hosts, treating them with a lot of suspicion and threatening them if they got too near. Clearly he was getting too vicious, and now that he was able to wander (and consequently mess) around the house, he would have to move. He was transferred, not without incident, to the porch. In the process he managed to bite Emma and sweep the desk clear of papers and plants with a few deft swipes of his left wing as she carried him out. Even now he was a nuisance. He threatened visitors to the door, despite being penned in. This was not entirely unbeneficial. He managed to clear away one tramp, two early carol singers and a life insurance salesman. Then he escaped into the garden. The family had had enough and were content to leave him there.

Eric was content too. It was three days since he had arrived, and though he was not right yet he was well on the road to recovery and his confidence had already returned. He had still got three others of his kind uppermost in his memory. In particular he had a score to settle with the two of them.

He was cautious as he sidled down the garden. The three occupants stared at him equally cautiously. They were not sure what to make of him. He was not as big as them and his colouring was different. Luigi and Flymo moved behind Aggro. Luigi pecked Flymo out of his way so that he could adopt a safer position. Aggro lowered his head and hissed at Eric, who heeded the warning and stopped.

Aggro had all the personality and poise of a Texan gunslinger ready to draw. Eric walked round to the side

and pretended to nibble at the grass, as if he did not care. Despite his stance, Aggro was not sure about squabbling with this unknown quantity, especially now he was looking stronger than when he first appeared. He was fooled by Eric's gesture of indifference into believing that he (Aggro) had established that he was still the boss.

So it was that with no initial trouble Eric entered the world of the garden. He found that Flymo was the first to come near him and open any conversation.

"Hallo," was all she said. She felt curious but too nervous to want to take matters further.

"Who are you?" grunted Eric.

"Flymo."

"Flymo? Sounds a stupid name to me. So is the sing-song way you talk. That and your funny colour suggest you are one of those degenerate domestic breeds. To make matters worse, in your case, you are deformed. Your tail sticks out at 79 degrees to your line of bilateral symmetry and I expect you're too fat to fly."

"That's not true! Its only 78 degrees 32 minutes and 6 seconds. Anyway I can fly! Why, I weigh 4.545 kilogrammes and when Luigi attacked me once I got a metre into the air in one second to escape over the fence. Now, if a kilogramme is approximately 9.8 newtons, that means I present a downward force of 44.492 newtons and so the work I did was a force times distance of 44.492 joules and as I did it in one second that means I produced 44.492 divided by 769 which equals 0.0578570 horse-power. I'm afraid I'm not very good at working things out to more than 6 significant figures but if you'll give me time I can ..."

" ... tell me it's 0.0578569570871 to 12 significant figures. You're fair at maths and you can do a lot of talking but you aren't a patch on me."

Eric went on to boast of his achievements and endurance at flying. Flymo listened with fascination as her mind worked out the statistics. It was not just the maths that attracted her to this new arrival with his strange accent. Neither was it his looks or physical prowess. Truth to tell, he was not much to look at. He was smaller than most ganders she had met, too, but looks are not always the most important thing. True, he had been rude at first, but when you compared that with what most other geese had been like to her it was trivial. What impressed her was that he did not bully her. He actually talked to her as if she was worth speaking to, even if he was bragging a bit. What clinched it in her mind that Eric was Mr. Perfect was when the inevitable clash with Aggro occurred.

It happened before Eric had even finished speaking. Aggro may not have liked either of them but he resented seeing them enjoy each others' company without being in on it. He decided to disrupt proceedings and re-establish his status by pecking Flymo. Eric was still an unknown quantity and it might be easier to impress him than take him on. Eric would have been unconcerned about what Aggro did to Flymo at other times but he was extremely irritated at having the best bit of boasting he had ever done in his life interrupted. Without thinking he pulled Aggro off Flymo by grabbing his neck firmly in his own bill. Eric continued by shaking Aggro's neck backwards and forwards, hard and fast. Aggro's head had no alternative but to follow his neck until Eric's anger had subsided.

On being released, Aggro was well and truly discombobulated. He had a vague recollection that his brains once lived in his head. He was not sure quite where they had gone to at that moment. He had also suffered from Eric's wings. Wings that can carry a gander hundreds of miles in all weathers know how to thump.

Aggro staggered off to recover, muttering some naughty words as he went. The spectators only managed to catch the phrase,

"He's a brute."

"Oh, isn't he just!" admired Flymo.

11. A Change of Heart

Flymo was convinced that Eric must be the ultimate gander any goose could dream of. She followed him around everywhere. She talked, or rather listened, to him a lot and he kept her free of Aggro and Luigi's unwelcome attention. She felt impressed to discover that he was a real wild goose. How wonderful. His stories were so dramatic, and to think that she believed his clan were extinct! Sadly, it only took a couple of days for her to discover that her romantic ideas were an illusion. Her admiration of Eric was not reciprocated.

Eric's conscious thoughts were moving elsewhere. He had recovered very fast and now he was growing more and more restless every day. He took to flying around and trying to explore the neighbours' gardens. He liked what he found. It would have satisfied even the fussiest gourmet in the goose world. It left the owners of the gardens far from happy. It was not just the nuisance. Most of them were scared of him.

It took very little time for a decision to be made that this wild visitor would have to be released back where he was supposed to have been.

"We'll take his photograph as he was such an event in our year. Maybe even the Stroud News and Journal will be interested. It's an unusual story. Then we'll box him up and see what the Wildfowl Trust at Slimbridge can do with him. That should keep the neighbours happy and solve a few other problems," James decided.

He need not have bothered. Eric had already had a similar idea. He would find his way to wherever he should be under his own steam. Then he could rejoin his natural group and fly back to Iceland when the time came. He casually remarked upon it to Flymo, who was horrified. Surely not! Her life had been turned upside down in the few days she had known him.

"Eric! You can't be serious! What about me?"

"What about you?"

"Don't I come into your calculations? Surely I must mean something to you?"

"You? Well I'd never really thought about it. I suppose you've always been around and your company was alright. But no. I've got to go and you couldn't come too. It's nothing personal, but you aren't built to live like a wild goose. It's not just that you're too heavy to fly ..."

"But I can fly! When I had to escape from Luigi I climbed a metre in one second. That's a better vertical take off than a Harrier jump jet despite its thousands of pounds thrust and ..."

"Hold on. Let me finish my sentence will you? I was going to say you're too heavy to fly *far*. On top of that you're too deformed to manage. A bit of your left foot is missing, your tail sticks out at 78 degrees 46 minutes and 19 seconds by my reckoning, and ..."

"Stop! I don't want to hear any more! I can't believe what you're saying. It seems that the only value I have is to be company while birds like you park here until you recover! What will my future be, if anything?"

85

Eric paused and looked seriously at Flymo. He had not realised how crucial he had been to her. Did she mean anything to him? He was not sure really. How could he tell?

The answer to both Flymo's and Eric's questions came over the wall that very moment.

"There you are!" snarled Fearless.

He had noticed Eric but chosen to ignore him. He was a small bird and might make a Christmas dinner later on. No. Here was the prize. As he had done before, Fearless seemed to paralyse Flymo with his piercing eyes. She was so petrified that she could not even squawk. She did not need to, for fate stepped in. Even from an egg she had been destined to survive against all the odds. She may have been gripped by Fearless's eyes as he advanced upon her, but piercing eyes have their limitations. While they were fixed on her, they could not give their attention to anything else.

Eric's thoughts went back to his first traumatic experience. He recognised the stance he had seen in the arctic fox who had killed his father. He felt the same instinct that his father had displayed over a vulnerable individual. He was not going to make his father's mistake of waiting for the predator to move first. A sudden fury exploded in him and he charged full pelt into Fearless.

Fearless was taken completely unawares as the wild gander struck. In a blind rage Eric seized the first thing he could in his bill. He got a firm grip on Fearless's ear. With remarkable power he beat Fearless mercilessly in the eye. He had the benefit of surprise, but Fearless quickly reacted. He did not have much choice. This was

 agony. There was nothing he could do about his ear, but he managed to catch the pitiless wing in his mouth and lock his carnivorous teeth deeply into it. Both animals were driven by pain to grind harder at the part of the other which they held.

They dragged each other around the garden in what appeared a hopeless compromise. Eric was tugging repeatedly at Fearless's ear while Fearless ground his jaws around as he shook Eric's wing. The contest was short and soon decided by motivation. Eric was fighting for life and had nothing to lose. Fearless was fighting for food and status. He was not desperately hungry and intense pain had replaced any other feelings. His only desire now was to get away. He released his grip on Eric and tried to run off. Eric, still driven by blind instinct, would not let go and got dragged along behind Fearless as he raced through the entrance to the pen. The badly mauled wing, now hanging at an unnatural shape and angle, met the wooden gatepost with a thud. Fearless howled in pain as the damaged ear, which had been towing Eric, was given a final tear. Even in his frenzy, Eric could not believe the agony he felt, as his mangled wing received its final punishment. He let go of Fearless, who did not hang around.

Daniel arrived to see what the row was all about. He was just in time to spot Fearless's brush disappearing behind the wall. That was a bit of a surprise but the sight of Eric was a shock. He was writhing across the garden with the remains of his ruined wing following pathetically behind.

"What are we going to do, Dad?" he asked, as he got his father to come and have a look

"I suppose we'll have to put him out of his agony. The trouble is that I'm not sure how. I've never killed a bird before. In theory you wring their necks. It's supposed to be quick and painless."

"It probably is if you do it properly but none of us knows what we're doing. Isn't there an alternative?"

"Well I've heard that you can strike them across the back of the neck with a cricket bat or maybe we could just hold his head under some water for five minutes and drown him?"

"No! That's horrible! What I mean is, isn't there any alternative to killing him?"

"What else is there? He's been badly mauled. His wing is hardly recognisable. He's in a state of shock and he's lost a lot of blood. The pain must be unbearable."

"We could try the vet, surely!"

"There's a limited amount he could do. He'd most likely only recommend putting him down. Anyway with me on Invalidity Benefit we can't afford bills like that. It's just not possible ... I mean ..."

James was staring at Eric's eyes. They did not have the glassy look which Hassle's had had as he died. They had an intense, gripping look. James did not know that Eric could understand what had been said. Eric was trying hard now to plead with James in a way he could understand. The only communication he could use was the appeal in his eyes. In a strange way James felt the message.

"Oh alright. Come on then. Let's get him down to Bowbridge "

Half an hour later they were in the Veterinary Surgery beside the canal.

"Look. I can understand your concern but I must give you the facts and the facts don't encourage what you're asking. This poor creature is seriously injured. In a shocked condition like this he's not likely to survive, even with our help."

"Yes, we've been through all this already and, hopeless as it may seem, we'd still like to give him this remote chance. Are you able to save him?"

"It's a slim possibility. But even if I could, have you thought of the consequences? These birds are used to flying hundreds of miles every year but this one will never fly again. Is it fair for him to go through the rest of his life like that? Is it right to keep such a wild creature in captivity? Will you be able to look after him properly? Have you seriously considered all these things?"

"We have. If it's at all possible, we'd like you to go ahead."

"Very well. I'll give it a go despite my doubts ..."

We'll leave Eric on the operating table and return to someone else who could use some surgery. What about Fearless? His ear was badly torn and soon got infected. In a short time, the infection won and the ear came right off. Fearless never again had his reputation. How could he when the other animals had given him a new name? They had dropped the "F" off his old one.

12. Fulfilment

Let us move on two years and see how the people and animals' fortunes are progressing.

James is sitting watching some of his geese in the graveyard at the Baptist Church. They have done a superb job of clearing the garden of weeds and keeping the grass down. Now they are turning their talents to reducing the workload in the churchyard. They have made good replacements for Cleopatra, the goat. James is watching them to make sure they do not eat the flowers on some of the graves. In practice he's doing more than that.

The strange illness that has dogged him for so long has been recognised. It is called myalgic encephalomyelitis, ME for short. It has no obvious cure but the geese are helping him to recover. It's because he's meditating on their ways. Their attitude to life has much to teach us. Let's see what is going on in a goose's mind:

"Think I'll eat a bit of grass. I fancy that bit. Perhaps I ought to nibble at a piece of clover for a change of taste. Now, while that settles into my crop I'll just stop and muse upon the world about me. While I'm about it, I fancy a drink. I'll pad along to the water trough and have a sip. That's good. Let's have another one. In fact it's so good I might as well put my head right under and have a good soak. That's it. Let's do it again and shake the water down my back. Lovely! Now let's watch the world go by again. I wonder what those people are doing in that garden over there? Let's go and have a look. Hmm. There's a different kind of grass over here. Not bad. It has a sweet taste to it. This weather is a bit hot. Think I'll give my feathers a ruffle. Ah. That's better. Looks like they could do with a preen. Yes, now that's an improvement. That was quite tiring. Mustn't overdo things. Think I'll have a nap, stick my head under my wing. Mmm ... nice and cosy. Now what shall I dream about?"

Stress and worry clearly are not in these geese's vocabulary. Perhaps that's why some live longer than people and are reputed to still lay eggs when they are over 100 years old. Just sitting and watching them makes their laid-back approach to life catching. James can feel life's stresses and strains falling away as he looks at them. They are making him better.

One gander who is not with them is Eric. He's still kept in the garden, where he may be the smallest of the group but he's the noisiest, and the boss. All this is despite his deformed wing too. To the surprise of everyone, especially the vet, Eric survived the operation. He quickly adjusted to having only one proper wing, but resented life in captivity for some time. To some extent he still does. He is not exactly domesticated. He accepts food but will happily bite the hand that puts it down, if it does not let go in time. He'll challenge most visitors to the garden. He hates being penned in.

On one occasion he actually led a raiding party out of the pen by sliding under the wire. The object of his raid was a picnic tea, which some visitors had just put out for

themselves. The visitors had hardly got started before they had to scatter in all directions as the four birds took over. They indulged in the fresh sliced bread as though they had never tasted anything so delightful before. That was not surprising. They had not. The jam was very popular, especially the aptly named "Gooseberry". Apart from a few pecks, the cake survived. No one seemed to like the chocolate flavour and certainly the cream was too rich. Such bread as was buttered was also spared. The greasy nature of it was too off-putting. Health food fanatics would definitely have approved.

Eric has reluctantly learnt to go into the shed at night, but he is always last in and first out. He gets over the humiliation of being locked in by claiming it is not so much to protect the group from foxes any more.

"It's to protect the foxes from me!" he boasts.

Earless would not argue. He keeps well away these days.

What of the central character in our story? Flymo is sitting nearby, under the hazel tree. She has her goslings all round her. She has just finished teaching them simultaneous equations. They are not ready for calculus yet. Now she is thinking how she has become a success story in several ways.

From her point of view, she has won the affections of the most impressive mate in the Stroud area. He does not mention her tatty state. With only one decent wing now, Eric is hardly in a position to judge, is he?

Despite their physical deformities, Eric and Flymo produced half a dozen normal looking goslings. Under their father's watchful eye they are all growing safely into handsome creatures. This has raised some scientific interest. The goose is fortunate not to be a deeply researched and specially bred creature like most farm animals. It has always been assumed, therefore, rather than proved, that domestic geese are simply a farmyard version of the wild greylag. This successful crossing of a wild and a domestic goose lends more scientific proof that this theory is correct.

Flymo stops her daydreaming as she notices that some visitors have come to the door. Daniel goes to see what they want. He soon returns with them.

"Here, Flymo. I've got an old friend come to see you. I'd better pen Eric in or he'll let his jealousy get the better of him!"

The imprisoned Eric is furious and tells the village so as he watches the stranger walk up to his mate.

"Hallo Flymo!" says David. "Do you remember me? I've come a long way and gone to a lot of trouble to find you."

Flymo answers by stepping into his lap and nuzzling her head against his chest. If only she could talk to him so that he could understand her! There is so much she could tell him.

"Oh David! I have missed you so much through all my suffering. It would have been totally different if you had been around. At one point I wished I was dead but that was before I realised how good life could be. It's turned out alright in the end. I've found a lovely place to live and a nearly perfect mate, who values me immensely. That's him making all the noise over there, by the way. I've reared a dozen fine children and now look over the wall. Can you see the machine the neighbour is using to eat his grass? I must be very important! Look what's written on the front! It's been named after me!"

95

About the Author:

Graham Hobbs was born in Enfield in 1953. He attended Enfield Grammar School where he was good at pole vault and mishaps, fortunately not at the same time. Outside of school he was a keen member of Boys Brigade and Crusaders, both of whom deserve a plug.

At Bedford College, in Regents Park, he obtained a degree in Botany and met his future wife, Yvonne. She introduced him to her native Gloucestershire where they are happily settled with their three children, Michael, Jennifer and Barbara.

Most of his working life, Graham has been a teacher. In addition he has done a variety of other jobs. The two most unusual, but nevertheless enjoyable, were helping on a dairy farm in the Arctic and pall bearing. His son says of the latter that his dad could even drive the dead round the bend.

Graham's interests include old things that still work, such as his car and motorbike, fossil hunting, entertaining overseas visitors, digging up his ancestors (metaphorically speaking) and playing his bagpipes. Fortunately, one neighbour is out a lot and the other comes from Glasgow.

On a more serious note, his Christian faith, his church involvement and family life are the most important aspects of his life, helping him to cope with his being ill with myalgic encephalomyelitis (M.E.). This book is dedicated to fellow sufferers. Achieve what you can within your limitations.